Don't Get Mad, Get Even

by
Lucy Jane Bledsoe

GLOBE FEARON EDUCATIONAL PUBLISHER
Upper Saddle River, New Jersey
www.globefearon.com

Project Editor: Brian Hawkes
Editorial Assistants: Jennifer Keezer, Jenna Thorsland
Art Supervision: Sharon Ferguson
Production Editor: Regina McAloney
Electronic Page Production: José López
Manufacturing Supervisor: Mark Cirillo
Cover Design: Sharon Ferguson
Illustrator: Ron Bell/S.I. International

Printed in the United States of America
1 2 3 4 5 6 7 8 9 10 03 02 01 00 99

ISBN 0-130-23287-4

GLOBE FEARON EDUCATIONAL PUBLISHER
Upper Saddle River, New Jersey
www.globefearon.com

Contents

1. Staying After School

Mrs. Well writes my name for all the class to see. W I L M A B U R N S. Big as day. That means I have to stay after school. I didn't do my homework. Again.

Sometimes I get so mad at Mrs. Well. She's harder on me than other kids. I think it's because she is part Cherokee like me. She doesn't let me get away with anything.

I don't care if I have to stay after school. What else is there to do? I don't play on any teams. I used to play in the band. But they stopped having band. Mr. Swimmer, the principal, said there was no money for it. We asked him why. But he just said that Mr. Singer, the head of all the schools in my city, said so. That was it. No more band. Why didn't they cut the baseball team? Or the science group? Why band?

I just don't care.

All I care about is summer. School is out in 4 weeks. Then I have all summer to have a good time.

It would be a better time if my brother Levi had not joined the Navy. He moved to Mississippi. Now I live with my mom. Dad lives in California with his new girlfriend. He has a new girlfriend every year.

Levi used to help me with my homework. He is my best friend. When he was home, I never had to stay after school.

After school, I go to Mrs. Well's room. I sit down and look at my homework. I'm not very good at reading and writing. My homework always takes too long. That's why I sometimes don't do it. Levi has a good head. He never had any problems with his schoolwork.

Today I do my homework as best as I can. Then I hand it in to Mrs. Well.

"Do you plan to finish school, Wilma?" she asks me.

"Why not?" I say. "I have 1 more year."

"**If** you pass your classes **this** year."

I can feel my face turn all red. "What do you mean?" I ask.

"From what I hear, this isn't the only class you may not pass," she says. "If you don't finish high school, what will you do with your life?"

Mrs. Well makes me feel all hot and mad. So I just walk out of her class. I know she is shaking her head. It's as if I'm not worth anything.

2. The Thing That No One Knows About Me

Mom gets home from work at 6:00. We turn on the TV and eat dinner from a can. She doesn't feel like cooking. Most days, I cook dinner. But I feel really bad tonight. The way Mrs. Well talked to me makes me want to die.

Mom never gets mad at me when I don't make dinner. She understands that some days you just can't do everything right. She doesn't ask any questions. We just eat out of a can and look at the news.

Mom and I look at the news every night. We want to see if any Americans go off to fight somewhere. We don't want Levi to have to do any real fighting.

There is more to why I like to look at the news.

No one knows this. But someday I'd like to be the woman who reads the news on TV.

I know. You have to go to college and everything to do that. So I'll never get to have that job. But even so, sometimes when Inez Ramos is doing the news, I think what it would be like if that was me.

I don't tell Mom about having to stay after school. I feel so scared about what Mrs. Well said. I might not even finish high school. What will I do then?

The thing is, the more scared I feel, the harder it is to do my homework. When I get scared, I can't think. Maybe I just will not go to school the next day. Mom would kill me.

Then I remember that first thing the next day is an all-school meeting. I can do my homework as the meeting is going on. This thought makes me feel better. After the news, I go to sleep.

3. I Don't Care About Anything

I can't believe it! Who do I see first thing the next day in school but Mrs. Well. She is walking down the hall toward me. I act as if I don't see her. She is just going to ask if I did my homework.

"Wilma." She stops me in the hall. "You're going the wrong way," she says. "The all-school meeting is this way."

I can't tell her I'm missing the all-school meeting to do my homework. So I have to turn around and walk with her to the meeting. I try to find a place to sit away from her. But she sits down right next to me. I want to die.

The principal, Mr. Swimmer, gets up to talk. He says, "I have some bad news. This is the last year Rivet High School will be open. Next year, each of you will have to take a bus to another school."

What? All the kids start talking at the same time. You would think the high school closing would make me happy. I can get out of this place at last. But I feel scared. Another high school? I have enough problems trying to stay in this one. I'm used to Rivet High.

Mr. Swimmer goes on. "This building is not safe. The city doesn't want us to be here another year. Too much needs to be fixed on the building, and there just isn't any money to do it. So the head of the city's schools, Mr. Singer, has ordered us out. We talked him into letting us finish out the school year."

I look at Mrs. Well. I can tell she has already heard this news. Her face is hard and mad-looking. Will she lose her job?

Some kids start laughing. But I feel as if someone has just hit me. First, they say there is no money for the one thing about school I liked—band. Now they say there is no money for our school at all.

People talk about kids not caring about school. One can't like school if there aren't enough books. In science class, there is only one book for every three kids. It's hard to do the work when I don't even have my own book. Now they are saying they can't even keep a school open.

Why should I do my homework if they can't even get enough books or schools?

Right then, I know what I'm going to do. I'm going to leave school. After all, Mrs. Well said I was not going to make it, anyway. I'll get a job. Maybe I'll join the Navy like Levi.

I don't care. I don't care about anything.

4. Levi's Letter

Mrs. Well writes my name for all to see again today. W I L M A B U R N S. All the kids know this means I didn't do my homework. They all know that means I have to stay after school. But I don't care. They are closing our school. I'm leaving anyway.

After school when I go into her class, Mrs. Well says, "What is it, Wilma? Is it about your brother moving out? I know you were very close."

I don't answer her. I just do my homework. Then I go home.

That night I turn on the TV. But Mom turns it off. She says, "I want to talk to you over dinner."

I don't look at her.

She says, "The principal called me at work today. He says you may not pass two of your classes."

"So?" I say.

"Don't you talk to me like that, Wilma," Mom says.

"Sorry," I say quietly.

"Why aren't you doing your schoolwork?"

No one understands. Levi was my best friend. Now he's gone.

"Talk to me, Wilma," Mom says.

"Who cares?" I tell her. "They are closing the school."

"Yes, I heard," she says. "You'll go to a new school next year."

I can tell by the look on her face that this does not make her happy. I don't tell her that I'm not going to the new school. I don't tell her that I'm going to leave school.

That night, instead of doing my homework, I write a letter to Levi. I'm a bad writer. But I can write well when I write to Levi.

Levi,

They are closing the high school! I can hardly believe it. They want me to go to another high school in the city for my last year. Forget it. I'm not going.

The more I think about it, this makes me mad. People never think about kids. They think they can just close the school. First, they take away band. Then they take away the whole school!

I don't like anything about life.

Wilma

A week later, I get a letter back from Levi.

Wilma,

What's the point in getting mad? Don't get mad, get even.

Levi

I can't stand it when Levi does this to me. Mom says Levi is a **man of little words**. I'll say. It's better when he's home. Then I can ask him what his words mean. What does his letter mean? Why did he only write two sentences?

Mom gets a letter the same day. In her letter, Levi says he is shipping out the next day. He will be at sea for six weeks. So I can't even write him back to ask, "What does **Don't get mad, get even** mean?"

5. My Meeting

Do you ever get the feeling that some people want all kids to go away for good? How can they just close Rivet High? Why do they think they can just ship us out to another school?

I can't stop feeling really mad. I keep reading Levi's letter over and over again. Each time I do, I feel something inside me turn over. He means I should fight back. But how?

I know what Mom would say: "Do your homework. Get all A's. Show them who you are."

I know Mom is right. But I can't do my homework when I feel so mad.

It makes me laugh that I don't want them to close the school. Just last week I thought I couldn't stand school. Maybe I'm changing my mind. This school is all I have. I don't have any idea what kind of job I can get when I get out of school. This school has been my life for three years. I have one more year here. I don't want to go to another school.

So I say this to myself: if they keep the school open, I'll work hard. I'll pass all my classes. But if they close Rivet High, I'm not going to another school.

Way down inside, I really do want to finish school. Mr. Swimmer said they were closing Rivet High. So I know what I have to do. I have to **make** them keep Rivet High open.

That night I make a big ad. At the top I write, **SAVE RIVET HIGH SCHOOL**. Then I write the ad. I show it to Mom.

At first, she can't believe that I made this ad. But then she says she is happy I did. She helps me fix the words that are wrong. Here is my finished ad:

"SAVE RIVET HIGH SCHOOL! Come to a meeting today after school. Let's talk about how we can keep Rivet High open. Don't let them push us out! Meet in the baseball field at 3:15."

I make ten more ads. The next day, I get up right when the sun does. I go to school way before classes start. I put the ads up all over the school halls.

Then I go to my classes. I feel happy. All day I hear kids talking about my ad. They are saying things like:

"Who do you think put it up?"

"That's a good idea! How can they close our school?"

"I'm happy someone is thinking about fighting back."

"I'm down for this one."

So at 3:15 I race out to the baseball field. I can't wait to get started. We will talk about ideas we have for keeping our school open. I sit in the field and wait for the other kids.

At 3:30, no one has come to my meeting.

Maybe they are talking to their friends before coming out here, or maybe they can't see me. So I stand up again. That way they can see me in the baseball field.

Then I have another idea. Maybe they can see me. Maybe no one is coming because they found out it's **me** who called the meeting. Why would anyone come to **my** meeting?

At 4:00, no one has come to my meeting. I feel sick.

At 4:00, no one has come to my meeting. I feel sick. I go back into the school. I walk through the halls and take down all the ads I put up.

Then I walk home real slow. I don't take the bus. I just walk. I have not felt so bad in all my life.

6. I'm Leaving School

I tell Mom I'm not going to school the next day. I tell her I'm not going to go to school ever again. What's the point? I'm not passing my classes. They are closing my school. I'm not going back ever again.

"Wilma," Mom says. "I know this is a hard time for you with Levi gone. But it's not like you to give up. You have always been a fighter."

"What's there to fight for?" I want to know.

"Yourself," Mom says. "Fight for yourself."

"What does **that** mean?"

"You know what it means. What would your brother say if you left school for good?"

Why did Mom have to talk about Levi?

"Just give me your word you'll finish this year.

Then we will talk about next year. OK?"

I'm quiet.

"Wilma," she says. "It'll break Levi up if you leave school. You know how he counts on you to take care of yourself now that he's gone."

"OK, OK," I scream. "I'll finish this year. After that, I'm through with school."

Mom looks away, but I can tell she is about to cry. I feel so bad. But how can I face the kids at school?

In school the next day, Luis comes up to me in the hall. I have never talked to Luis before in my life. He gets all A's. He knows all the answers in every class. He's a real science shark. People say he knows how to **make** computers.

Luis says, "I heard that you're the girl who put up the ads about saving Rivet High School."

"So?" I say.

"How did your meeting go?"

I look him right in the eye and say, "It was good. There were 100 people there."

Luis looks at me for a long time. He seems kind of hurt. "No, there were not," he says. "Why are you making things up?"

I start to walk away. I know he is just going to laugh at me with the other kids.

He comes after me. "No one came to the meeting," he says. "Right?"

"Good guess," I say.

"I wanted to come. But I had too much homework."

I laugh. "How much homework can you have?"

"Are you going to have another meeting?"

"With my dog," I say.

"Why are you like this?" he says. "You never just answer. You always have to make a crack."

"Why do you ask so many questions?" I say.

He stops walking. I can feel him looking at me as I walk down the hall.

Then I go into the girls' room. There I start to cry. I know he is laughing at me. I called a meeting for the first time in my life. No one came. I want to die.

7. Other Kids Come Through—Too Late

I told Mom I would finish out the school year. So, even after that bad talk with Luis, I have to go back to school the next day.

Right away, in science class, a kid named Tyrone comes up to me. He writes all the news for the school radio show. Everyone likes him. He has 100 friends.

"I heard about your meeting," he says. "I wanted to come, but I had to work on my radio show."

"No one came," I say. I don't want to talk about it anymore. I want to forget all about it.

"Are you going to have another meeting?"

"No."

"Let me know if you do," Luis says. "I'm into helping out. I mean, it isn't fair. Who do they think they are, closing our school? Good for you for trying."

Then in social studies class, Kay comes up to me. She plays on just about every girls' team in the school. She's a star on the swim team. She gets all A's, too. But Kay is mean sometimes. She doesn't like kids who she thinks aren't as good as she is. That's why I can't believe it when she says, "I like your idea about saving Rivet High. Do you think we really can?"

Then I see Luis standing there, too. He says, "A lot of kids want to help."

"Why didn't anyone come to the meeting?" I want to know.

"I didn't know who you were," Kay says. "I didn't want to come to just any meeting."

Kay doesn't like to hang out with the wrong people. I know that about her.

Kay goes on, "The swim team is going to take the city championship next year. If we go to a new high school, that's all gone. Besides, I want to run for office next year, too."

"Go on, girl," Tyrone says, walking up. "Go for the stars. Fastest swimmer. Most A's. Head of the class."

"Be quiet, Tyrone," she answers. But I can tell she likes Tyrone. Everyone likes Tyrone.

"Let's try again," Luis says. "Today after school. We can all try to talk to as many kids as we can."

"I already gave up," I say. "I don't think it will work." I'm scared of these kids. Kay is a swim team star and running for office. Luis is good in school. Everyone likes Tyrone.

"Come on," Kay says. "I can't stand the idea of going to another school our last year. It's not fair."

Luis says, "I'll talk to Mrs. Well. Maybe she will let us use her classroom."

"No way!" I say. "I don't want to go into Mrs. Well's class after school if I don't have to."

Luis doesn't know what I mean. He never has to stay after school. He **always** does his homework.

But Kay is in that class with me. She looks at me. I know she is thinking about working with someone who doesn't do her homework. But she says, "I see your point. Why not the baseball field, again? It's a warm, sunny day."

"Maybe," I say. "I might have something else I have to do."

8. The Principal Says Give It Up

At 3:15, I look out the school window. Luis, Kay, and Tyrone are all out on the baseball field. I walk out there slowly.

"Here she is!" Tyrone says. "The woman behind it all, chief of Save Rivet High School."

Everyone cracks up laughing. At first, I think they are laughing at me. But then I see they are just having a good time. So I laugh, too.

Tyrone puts an arm around me. He says, "Good idea, kid. Let's get going." Tyrone is open and friendly. I like him.

Luis steps in between me and Tyrone. What's his problem?

Tyrone says again, "Let's get started."

"Who is that?" Kay says.

We all look at another kid walking toward us. I know him. His name is César. He has had a lot of problems. Last year, they put him out of school because of drug problems.

Then Kay says, "We don't want him working with us."

"Why not?" I say.

"You know why not. He has drug problems."

Who does Kay think she is?

I say, "The drug problems were last year. He's over that."

I can't believe I'm talking back to Kay. Then César is standing with us.

I say, "This is a meeting about saving Rivet High School."

"That's why I'm here," he says with a big smile.

Kay turns her back to him. She says, "What should we do first?" She sounds cold.

Luis says, "Mr. Swimmer said that there were problems with the building. We have to find people to fix them."

"That will take a lot of money," I say.

"We have to get people to do the work for free," César says.

"Oh, right," Kay says to him. "As if people are just going to do things for free, César."

"Hold up, Kay," Tyrone says. "Why are you getting on César's back?"

César looks at Kay with hard eyes.

"Because we don't need his kind of problems. I'm sorry. Maybe that sounds cold. If we are going to save Rivet High, we have a lot of work to do. We need people who can give their all."

"This isn't a swim meet," I say. "You don't have to win anything, Kay. We all go to Rivet High. We all have our own ideas about why we want to save it."

Kay keeps quiet.

"OK," Luis says. "We need to raise money. That's first. How can we raise money?"

I say, "I think we have to get to people's feelings. People are always saying kids don't care about school. We are saying, **We care. We want our school**. We have to make people hear that. If they believe in kids, then they better put their money in us."

"She's right," Luis says. "We have to make

people see we want our school. Then they will give us money."

"How much money do we need?" Tyrone asks.

Luis says, "Maybe Mr. Swimmer is in his office now. Let's go see if we can find out."

"Good idea," says Tyrone.

We all go back into the building. We find Mr. Swimmer in his office. We tell him what we want to do. He laughs.

César asks, "What are you laughing at?"

Mr. Swimmer stops laughing right away. César should not talk to the principal in that way. Maybe Kay was right. Maybe César will just make problems for us.

"Well, now," Mr. Swimmer says. "I just don't want you kids to put a lot of hope in something that can't happen. Mr. Singer said the school is closing, so the school is closing."

"But if we can fix the building," I say. "Then why should it close?"

"It would take lots and lots of money. About $150,000. How do you kids think you can get that?" I see him look at César, meaning not your way.

We all look at one another. $150,000! That's more money than I've ever even thought about.

But Luis says, "No problem. When do we have to have it?"

Mr. Swimmer says, "School opens in the fall. That's in 16 weeks, as you know. Kids, no one said you can do this. I'm sorry. The school is closing."

9. I Get Mad—Again

I walk out of Mr. Swimmer's office with Luis, Kay, Tyrone, and César.

"We gave it a try," Kay says. "I guess we're going to some other high school next year."

"They will have a swim team," I say, trying to make her feel better.

"No one will know me," she says. "How can I run for office?"

Luis is quiet.

Tyrone says to Kay, "You aren't the only one who has to make changes and give things up, you know."

César says, "Are you all giving up that easy?"

"He's the principal," Kay says.

"César is right!" I jump in. "Mr. Swimmer didn't

say we **can't** do it. He just said he didn't want us to get our hopes up."

"Forget it," Kay says. "That means no."

I feel that fire come up in me again. The way I feel mad. I have had it with people saying no to me. This is the only school we have.

Then I think of Levi's letter: **"Don't get mad, get even."**

"Look," I say. "All of you can do what you want. I'm going to fight for my school. I don't have band, or swim team, or science group, or any office to run for. But I want to have my last year at Rivet High."

Everyone stops walking. They can't believe this is me talking this way.

"All of you can give up," I say, walking ahead of them. "But I'm not."

That night Mom is out with some guy who she goes out with sometimes. I can't stand him. I wish Mom would meet someone I like.

I work on my homework a little. Then I look at the TV. I feel as if I'm the one in a ship at sea, not Levi. I'm scared. How can I save Rivet High all by myself?

10. We Go Out On Strike

On Saturday, Luis calls and says, "Come meet over at my house. I have an idea."

"I thought you were giving up," I say.

"How can I let you take on the fight all by yourself?" he asks.

I smile, but he doesn't know this because he can't see me. "OK," I say. "I'll be over."

When I get there, I find out Luis has called Tyrone, Kay, and César, too. Then he tells us his idea.

"I think we should hold a strike. We will still go to our classes. But before school every day we will go out on strike."

We work all day with the paints. We write BIG.

"DON'T CLOSE RIVET HIGH"

"Before school every day we will go out on strike."

"SAVE RIVET HIGH SCHOOL"

"DON'T SHIP US OUT"

"KEEP OUR SCHOOL OPEN"

The first day of the next week, we get to school long before classes start. We walk around and around the school holding up our writing. Cars on the streets see us. Some of them call out things like, "Way to go!", or "I'm with you all the way!"

Then I see Mrs. Well drive up. Oh no, I think. Here it comes. I'll have to stay after school again.

She walks right up to me. Then she puts an arm around me. "That's the way, Wilma!" she calls out. "You let me know if there is any way I can help." Then she walks into the building.

"Did you hear that?" I say to Luis. "Mrs. Well wants to help."

The next day, five more kids join us on our strike. It's not **really** a strike because we do go to class. But it's like a strike. Then the next day, 20 **more** kids join us. By the last day of the week, 150 kids are walking around holding up writing that says, "SAVE RIVET HIGH SCHOOL!"

That day, Mr. Swimmer comes up to me. He says, "Listen, Wilma. I know you mean well. But you are getting the hopes up of all these kids. I already told you. Rivet High is closing. That's that."

Just then I see a big truck drive up. KXED TV is painted on the side of the truck.

Tyrone calls out, "It's the TV people!"

Mr. Swimmer says, "Now you have done it."

I can't believe it. The TV people. Then Inez Ramos herself gets out of the truck. She walks right up to us.

"Who is running this show?" she asks with a big smile.

Mr. Swimmer works his way through the kids. "I'm the principal here," he says. "I just want to say—"

"I would like to talk to one of the kids," Inez Ramos says, cutting him off.

Luis says, "Wilma started this. Talk to her."

"No," I say, feeling scared. But Inez Ramos comes right up to me.

"What gave you the idea to try to save Rivet High School?" she asks me.

"Am I going to be on TV?" I ask.

Inez Ramos laughs and says, "Maybe."

Then something makes me feel strong. I start talking. "I have never done very well in school," I tell her. "I didn't think I would ever care if this school closed. But on the day Mr. Swimmer said Rivet High was closing, I felt something new. I started thinking about what I wanted out of life. How can I have a life, a good job, if I don't even have a school? If kids are just shipped around? What counts in life? I think kids count. We are here to tell everyone: WE COUNT."

I can hear all the kids screaming, "You tell them, Wilma! Save Rivet High!"

I keep talking to Inez Ramos. It's as if the words are coming from someone else. I can't stop. I tell her, "When I told my brother about how mad I was they were closing Rivet High, he said, "**Don't get mad, get even.**" Some kids might think that means do something violent. But for me it means it's time to start working for what we want. If they will not fix our school, **we** will."

When I finish, Inez Ramos says, "That was Wilma Burns at Rivet High School, and I am Inez Ramos for KXED. Tom, back to you."

Luis, Kay, Tyrone, and César all laugh and

laugh. After all, I'm the kid who doesn't do her homework. I'm the kid who doesn't play on any teams. I'm the kid who hardly talks. Now listen to me. I sound as if I run this school.

Inez Ramos smiles, too. She says, "Good job. I think you will look really good on the air." Then she gets in her truck and drives off.

All the kids start calling out my name: "Wilma! Wilma! Wilma!"

Mr. Swimmer looks at me and just shakes his head. He doesn't look mad. He just looks as if it is all too much for him. He puts his head down and pushes through the group of kids. I see him go into the school. I feel sorry for him. Even if we don't win, it feels a lot better to fight for something, to believe in something, than to give up hope. I don't think Mr. Swimmer has hope about anything.

11. I'm on TV

I make a really good dinner that night. When Mom comes home, I don't say a thing to her. At 6:00, we get our dinners. Then we put on the news like we always do.

First thing on the news is my face as big as day. Inez Ramos is standing next to me. She says, "With me today is Wilma Burns from Rivet High School." Then there is the part of me talking about everything. They put everything I said on the air.

Mom stops eating. Her mouth falls open. She can't believe it. Me, Wilma Burns, on TV, talking as if I'm running this city or something.

Then Mom jumps up and throws her arms around me. "That's my girl!" she says. "I wish Levi could see you now."

She is about to cry. Then she says, "When you were a little girl, you were always a fighter. After your dad left, I was scared all the fight went out of you. Wilma, I want you to know who you are and what you want."

"I think maybe I'm getting there, Mom," I say. "I'm trying."

Mom throws her arms around me again. Even I cry a little.

Then I get a call. I answer, and a man says, "I would like to speak to Wilma Burns."

"Who is this?" I say. It could be some joke call.

"Mr. Singer, head of the city schools."

My eyes get all big, and Mom says, "Are you OK? Who is it?"

I want to hang up. But I have gone this far. I might as well see what he wants.

"This is Wilma," I say.

"I saw you on the news," he says. "If only we had 2,000 kids in the schools like you."

"What?" I say.

"You are just what this city needs. I want to work with you. What can I do to help?"

"But you're the one closing the school," I say.

"We have big money problems. Before anything else, I want to save people's jobs. So the only thing I could see to do was close Rivet High and move everyone who works there to other schools. I didn't see any other way out. I don't want to close Rivet High. If we can keep it open, I'm all for it. You tell me: how can I help?"

"First," I say, thinking fast. "We need to know all the things that need to be fixed in the building."

"I can get you that," he says. "I can also help you work through the city."

"You mean if we can get the money, we can keep Rivet High open?"

"I can't say yes. But I'm not saying no. I don't want to do anything to get in your way."

After telling Mom, I call Luis. He is really happy about the call from Mr. Singer. Then Luis and I talk for a long time about other things. He says I sounded good on TV. Then he says, "You looked good, too."

I want to say, "What does that mean?" But I don't say anything. I don't have to because then he says, "I mean you look really pretty."

"Oh," I say. Then I feel as if I want to die. So I say, "I want to be like Inez Ramos some day."

He doesn't laugh. He says, "You would be good at that job."

Then he tells me a long story about going fishing with his dad. They caught ten fish. After that we hang up.

"What's making you smile so much?" Mom says.

I can't believe how fast everything has turned around. Two weeks ago, I was going to leave school, and I didn't think I had any friends. Now look at my life!

12. Big School Problems for Me

There is one week of school left. I have another idea. Why not start up the school band? It can help raise money.

I call another meeting. This one is for all the kids who want to play in the band. I ask Mr. Farmer, who used to run the band, to come. He says he will help us and for no pay.

On the last day of school, Mr. Swimmer, the principal, calls me into his office.

"Wilma," he says. "You did not pass two of your classes. Why is that?"

I don't know what to say.

"Answer me, Wilma."

"My brother Levi used to help me with my homework. He is in the Navy now. He doesn't live at home."

"That's not a good answer. I think you have been putting too much time in on this Save Rivet High thing. What's the point in saving the school if you can't pass your classes?"

I don't have an answer to that.

He goes on, "I want to see you finish school. You have a good head, Wilma. You have to do the work."

I look down at my hands. I had been feeling so good, too.

Then he says, "I'm sorry about the high school closing. But there is no point in your putting more time into it. This band thing, too, isn't worth your time."

I say, "But Mr. Singer says he wants to help. He is behind us."

"Mr. Singer is happy to see you kids working for something you believe in. But I don't think he's being fair letting you go so far with it. He knows as well as I know that you can't raise $150,000. You could throw away your summer working on this and have nothing to show for yourself next year. Do you know how much money $150,000 is?"

"Yes," I say. But I don't really. I know it's a **lot** of money.

"You better think about passing your classes so you can finish high school, Wilma. That's what you better do."

I leave his office feeling bad. Then I see Mrs. Well coming down the hall.

"Wilma," she says. "I want to talk to you."

"I know," I say. "I didn't pass two of my classes, your class and social studies."

"Come into my room," she says. I go in and sit down. She says, "You have a lot of fight in you. You also are a good thinker. What is keeping you from doing your schoolwork?"

"The reading is hard for me," I say. "I do well with numbers and in science. It's just that social studies has so much reading."

"You can make up the classes in summer school," she says. "I'm working over at City College this summer. You can be in my classes. You will have to work hard to pass. But I'd like to help you. You will still have time to work on Save Rivet High."

I look up fast. Summer school with Mrs. Well? I don't know if I like that. I can just see her writing my name up for people to see all summer long.

"I don't know," I say.

"You need to pass these two classes to finish high school, Wilma. You have too much going for you to stop now. What's the point in saving Rivet High if you are not going to finish school?"

She has a point there. It's just that I'm scared to take those classes. What if I **still** don't pass them?

"OK," I say quietly. Because way down inside I want to pass those classes. That way, if Rivet High stays open, I will be ready for my last year.

Mrs. Well smiles. I can see that she really isn't so mean. She works kids hard because she believes in us.

13. Raising Money

The first Saturday after school is out, the new band gets together in the school car lot. We start to play. We have a lot of work to do.

Tyrone, Luis, César, Kay, and I have put together a car wash. Some other kids come to help. We wash cars all day. The band plays all day, too. We make lots of money because each car wash is $10. People pay that much because they want to help us save Rivet High. Some people stay and listen to the band after they get their car washed. We make over $2,000.

Then we have a meeting the next Saturday. I'm really happy about all that money, but César says, "$2,000 is nothing. We need $150,000. We have to think of a way to make more money faster."

"You mean selling drugs?" Kay says.

"Hold up, hold up," Luis says. "You didn't need to say that."

"We have worked real hard," Kay puts in. "I don't like César acting as if the money we have is nothing. If he has good ideas, I want to hear them."

"I do have a good idea," César says. His eyes burn a hole in Kay. "My dad builds houses. He is out of work. He says he will do some of the work on the school building for free. Maybe we can get other people to work for free."

"That's a good idea!" I say. "After all, we aren't going to make $150,000 in the next eight weeks."

"We still have to buy things like the new windows and the new walls," Kay says. "That takes money—a lot of money."

Tyrone says, "Paying people to do the work is what takes the most money. With the car wash money and other money we have raised, we have about $3,000. That's a start for buying new windows and other small things. We can make more money."

Then Luis says, "I have another idea. We should get Wilma back on the news. People gave us money after seeing her on the news." He smiles at me.

"No way," I say.

"You liked being on the news, and you know it," Tyrone laughs.

"OK, first, we have to make KXED TV want to put us on the air. We have to do something to get on the news," Luis says. "You're the news-man, Tyrone. What do you think we should do?"

"I think we should use César's idea. Ask his dad and others to start doing the work on the school. We will help them. The TV people will like that. You know, kids fixing their own school. We'll call them to come see us doing it."

"That's good," I say.

"My dad can help us on Saturday. We can use the $3,000 to buy the windows," Luis says.

"You call Inez Ramos," Luis says to me. "Tell her what we are doing."

"No way," I say again.

"Way," Tyrone, César, and Luis all call out together.

That night Luis calls me again. "Have you called Inez Ramos?" he asks.

"It's Saturday night," I say. "I can't call her now."

"I know," Luis says. Then he laughs. "I had to have something to say for why I was calling you."

I can't believe that Luis likes me.

We talk for a long time. Then he asks if I want to go to a baseball game with him next week.

I can't believe it. Me going out with a guy who gets all **A**'s.

"I don't know," I say. "I'll think about it."

Then I feel bad because he says real fast, "OK, I have to go."

I think I hurt his feelings by not just saying, "Yes." So I call him right back. I say, "OK, I would like to go to the baseball game."

I can hear him smile.

14. Going Out With Luis

César's dad, Mr. Cruz, comes to the next Saturday meeting.

"We had a union meeting two days ago," he says. "Some of us said they would come help." He puts an arm around César as he says this.

With a dad like that, it's hard to understand why a kid like César had those drug problems. But then people may say the same thing about me not passing my classes.

Workers from the union show up. Some are good with windows, some with pipes, others with walls. A lot of the building's problems are not hard to fix. They just take time. The union workers show us how to do things. We all get to work.

We stop to eat at around 12:00. My mom comes

by with a lot of food. She's a really good cook, and I feel happy.

"Mom, this is Mr. Cruz," I say. They shake hands.

Mom says, "What would we do without you? It's so good of you to help the kids. This is going to work. I know it."

Mr. Cruz smiles. I like him.

After eating, I get to work on putting in a window. Luis and Mr. Cruz help.

I hear a woman say, "Wilma Burns?"

I turn around, and there is Inez Ramos from KXED TV. The TV people came!

"I'd like to put you on the air again," she says. "You were something last time."

"She was," Luis puts in.

So Inez Ramos asks me to talk on the air about what we are doing. I introduce Mr. Cruz and his friends. I tell how they are doing this work for free. I tell how we had to get the OK from Mr. Singer and that he is behind us all the way. Then I say how we need a lot more money. We still have to buy the doors, pipes, and paint. Rivet High will close if we don't get another $30,000 in the coming weeks.

The TV people came!

"Way to go," Inez Ramos says after I finish. "This is a hot story." She gets into the KXED TV truck. "You'll see yourself on the 6:00 news."

Then the TV people leave.

We get a lot of work done that day. We tell Mr. Cruz and his union friends how happy we are they are helping us. I see Mom giving Mr. Cruz the left over food. Then we go home.

That night, Luis comes over to my house to look at the news. I can't believe it's me on the air.

Then Luis and I go to the baseball game. We get hot dogs and drinks. We have a really good time.

Driving home, I tell him, "I didn't pass two of my classes. I have to take them over in summer school. They start next week."

Luis looks like he can't believe this. He says, "You are a good thinker. You have all the good ideas for saving the school. Why didn't you pass those classes?"

"I can write good letters to my brother Levi. But when I try to do my homework, my head doesn't work."

Luis doesn't say anything for a long time. I think I know what he is about to say. I say, "Most of the girls you go out with get all **A**'s, don't they?"

"I go out with so many girls, how would I know," he says.

I look over at him fast. He is smiling. That was a joke. I smile, too.

He says, "I want to be out with you."

That makes me feel good. So then I tell him, "I'm scared I will not pass my summer school classes."

"I'll help you," he says. He says it in such a friendly way, I just about believe him.

That night I write a long letter to Levi. The writing is not hard at all. I tell him all about trying to fix Rivet High. I even write to him about Luis.

15. A Thief Takes All Our Money

Lots and lots of people saw me the other night on TV with Inez Ramos. KXED TV got bags and bags of letters. People sent in over $5,000. We can't believe it.

"You looked good on TV," Luis says again. "I think you should tell Inez Ramos you want to work in TV."

"Oh, right," I say. "As if she cares what I want to do."

It's good to get more money. We keep using it to get things we need for the school building. The work goes fast. But there is lots more to do.

Every Saturday we have a car wash. The band plays every Saturday, too. People come every week and get their cars washed.

One Saturday, Inez Ramos comes to put the car

wash on TV. After that, even more people come to us to get their cars washed.

We keep making money. Kay keeps the money for us at her house.

One day after my summer school classes, I go over to Rivet High to help work on the building. Kids come every day to help.

I'm just starting to hold a pipe for a friend of Mr. Cruz's, when Kay comes running up.

"The money!" she screams. "It's gone!"

We all stop what we are doing. "What?" Tyrone says. "What are you talking about?"

"Someone took the money. I had it in a metal box in my room. It's gone."

Then she turns on César. She says, "We are the only ones who know I had it." She keeps looking at César.

"That's not fair," I say. Kay hasn't said a word about César. But we can all see what she is thinking.

César is holding some window glass. He throws it down, and it smashes. He walks out of the room. I can tell he is mad.

"See?" Kay says. "See? I told you he has a problem. Look how he acts. Would he have done that if he didn't take the money?"

"Kay," Luis says. "César's dad is doing all this work for free. If it weren't for him, we wouldn't be anywhere."

"You know as well as I do about the drug friends he has. He was put out of school last year. He still hangs out with the same kids."

I put my face in my hands. I just hope César's dad is far enough away so he can't hear this.

"Are you trying to say that César took that money?" Tyrone asks. "Because if you are saying that, and if you're wrong, then—"

"If you don't believe me," Kay says hotly, "then you tell me how César got that new car."

We all look at one another.

"What new car?" Luis says.

"The one he is driving today."

We all run to the window. We see César taking off out of the car lot. He is driving a new car.

We don't say anything for a long time. I think hard. Then I say, "You don't know César took that money. He's still my friend."

16. César's Car

That night I tell Mom about the money and César's new car. She says, "People are always pointing at other people. No one knows how he got the money for the car."

Mom is right. She has good ideas about people.

Tonight Luis is coming over to help me with my homework. Mom is cooking dinner. She likes Luis—a lot.

When he gets here, he and my mom hit it right off. He tells her that her cooking is good. She likes that.

After dinner, she leaves us to do my homework. Luis is different from Levi. Levi used to tell me the answers a lot. Luis makes me work them out myself. He is really good at showing me how. He keeps saying I have a really good head on me. He doesn't understand why I don't do better in school. I don't know what to tell him.

At about 9:00, I get a call. It's Kay.

She says, "I have some good news."

"What?"

"I found the money."

"You **did**?"

"My dad found it in my metal box. He took it and put it in the bank. He said no one should have that kind of money sitting around."

"He's right," I say.

"I guess I better call César and tell him I'm sorry."

I'm glad she thought of that on her own. "I guess you had better," I say.

After I say good-bye, I tell Luis. We are happy. I didn't think César took that money. But I have to say that new car didn't look right.

Luis and I go for a walk after doing my homework. "Let's go over to César's," he says. So we walk all the way there.

It is just about 11:00 at night. César is outside

working on his car. He has big lights up so he can see what he is doing.

"Like it?" he asks.

"Yes," I say. "It looks good. How does it drive?"

"Good," he says. Then he makes a face. "Kay thought I took the money."

I don't know what to say.

César goes on. "She called to say she was sorry. She never really came out and said she thought I took the money. Not to me. But I know that is what she was thinking."

"Kay is just kind of jumpy," I say.

"I guess so," César says.

"This is a real class car," Luis says.

César says, "I have been buying parts for a long time. I got the body last week. I just got to drive it for the first time this week. It has taken me years to build this car. It's pretty, isn't it?"

"I say it is."

César's dad comes out of the house. "Don't you think you better get some sleep—" he starts. Then he sees me and Luis.

"Oh, how are you doing?" he says. He looks at me for a long time. "How is your mom?" he asks.

"Why do you want to know?" I say.

"Just asking," Mr. Cruz says.

César smiles at me. I smile back. I guess Mr. Cruz likes my mom. I guess that is OK.

17. Time Is Running Out

Summer is just about over. We keep washing cars. We keep fixing the building. The band keeps playing all over the city. KXED TV keeps doing stories on us. I go on the air a lot. I get used to it. We raise lots of money—about $30,000. The problem is we still need another $20,000, even with Mr. Cruz and his union friends doing the work for free.

It is four weeks before school starts again. Mr. Singer calls a meeting. About 500 kids and lots of moms and dads meet in the school.

Mr. Singer looks like he needs some sleep. He has been working hard with us all summer long. Sometimes he even helps with the building. Most of the time he talks to people in the city. He helps move things along.

Now he says, "I don't know how to tell you kids

this. The city says they have to make a move. They have to know where you all will be in school in the fall. School starts in four weeks. But the city says the building has to be ready in two weeks, or you can't stay here."

"If we don't have the money to have the school fixed in two weeks, Rivet High will close."

Everyone jumps up.

"That's not fair," my mom calls out. "These kids have been working so hard. They are just about there. Two weeks isn't enough time. We can't make $20,000 in two weeks."

"I don't want to swim for another school!" Kay says. She is always thinking about herself.

I feel bad. All this work, and they are still going to close the school.

After the meeting, Mom says, "Why don't we all meet at our house and talk about it. You should come, too," she says to Mr. Cruz.

So Tyrone, Kay, Luis, César, Mr. Cruz, Mom, and I go home. We talk late into the night.

"We can't make that kind of money washing cars," Tyrone says.

"No way," César says.

"I think we have to give up," I say. "There is just no other way."

Everyone looks at me. I have been the one who would not give up all along. But we have done all we can.

Luis gives me a long, hard look. I know what he is thinking. I told him that I was going to leave school if Rivet High closes. It feels all dark inside me. We did everything we could do.

No one has an answer, so they all go home. Mr. Cruz smiles at my mom before he goes. "We have some good kids, don't we?" he says.

"We do," Mom answers.

18. Two Weeks to Raise $20,000

The next day César and his dad show up when Mom gets home from work. "We want to take you out to dinner," Mr. Cruz says.

Mom looks around as if he is asking someone else.

Mr. Cruz laughs. "You and Wilma. We have an idea."

At dinner, Mr. Cruz says, "Tell them, César."

César looks up from his dinner. He says, "I have been working on that car for four years. I've put in only the best parts. I think I can get $20,000 for it. I want to sell the car and give the money to the school. After school opens, we can raise enough money to pay me back."

"You can't do that," I say. "That car is your life."

"I know," he says. "But I can get the money back if we work all year trying to raise more. Then I can build another car. I like doing the work. I could use the money, too."

After dinner, Mom and Mr. Cruz say they are going for a drive. César and I say we will walk over to Luis's family's apartment to tell him the news.

As we walk, César says, "I think your mom and my dad want to start going out together."

This is hard to take in! But Mom does seem to like Mr. Cruz.

"What if they get married?" I ask. "Will that make you my brother?"

"Is that a problem?" César laughs.

"No, it's not," I say. "I think I would like that."

"Well," he says. "Your mom would be getting a good man in my dad."

"Ha!" I say. "Your dad would be getting the best in my mom."

We laugh. Then we get to Luis's apartment. He is home. We tell him the news about César selling his car.

19. Selling César's Car

We put ads up all over the city. The ad shows a picture of César's car. We say we will be selling it in the school car lot on Saturday. It will go to the man or woman who puts up the most money.

"What if no one goes over $5,000?" Tyrone asks. "Do we have to give away César's car for that?"

Everyone looks at Luis. He knows all the answers. "I think we do," he says. "We just have to make it so that people know this car is worth a lot of money."

"We have to get everyone all worked up. I think the band should be playing," I say.

"What good is the band?" asks Kay. "All you play is hard rock."

No one answers her. We are used to her being that way.

"Who is going to sell the car?" César asks.

"You should," I say. "It's your car."

"I don't know if I want to talk in front of so many people."

"Yes, you do," Luis says.

It is the day of the car sale. We have 1 week to raise the $20,000. If we don't get it today, that will be that.

The band starts playing. Mrs. Well comes to the car sale. So does Mr. Singer and even Mr. Swimmer. There are about 100 people there.

First, as the band plays, everyone looks at the car. We have people standing all around it so no one can hurt the paint job. César answers people's questions. He takes people who want to go for test rides.

KXED TV is there again. Inez Ramos is talking to lots of people on the air.

César stands up on a big box and starts calling out, "Do we have any buyers today?"

He is like me. After he gets going, he doesn't mind talking in front of all those people.

A man calls out, "$2,000!"

César laughs. "Are you kidding? I have $2,000. Do I hear $5,000?"

"$5,000!" calls out an old man who is wearing red. I smile. He looks like he has lots of money. Maybe he'll go up to $20,000 after awhile.

It is very quiet. I look around. No one puts up a hand. No one says a thing. Luis and I look at one another. It can't stop here.

César says, "I hear $5,000. Do I hear $6,000?"

No one says a thing. Then everyone seems to be screaming numbers.

It's finally up to the asking price. César starts, "For $20,000, it is going—going—gone—to the man in the red!"

The man runs up to the box to stand next to César. He has a big smile on his face. He really likes this car.

I can't believe we did it. We just raised $20,000.

20. Two New Jobs

It takes $20,000 to buy the rest of the pipes, paints, and wood that we need. We will work the rest of the year to make the money back to give to César.

The day the man drives César's car away, we all go over to see it off.

"How do you feel?" I ask César.

He says, "I feel like crying. But at the same time, I'm happy. What can I say?"

We work on the school building. We get all the work done just a week before classes start.

Then a good thing happens. Mr. Singer tells Mr. Cruz that the city is giving him a job. He is going to be a builder for the city.

Not only that, but Mrs. Well tells me I have

passed my summer school classes. I get a **B** and a **B+**. I'm ready to do my last year in high school.

That same week, I get a call from Inez Ramos. "I want to have a meeting with you," she says. "Can you come down to the KXED TV offices?"

"I can do that," I say.

She walks me through all the offices of KXED TV. I can't believe I'm there. We sit down in the news room.

"You are very, very good on the air," she says. "The story on Rivet High is just about over. But we don't want to lose your face on the air. How would you like to do a kids' look at the news on my show?"

My mouth falls open. I can't even talk.

"We are thinking of a show that would air every other week. You would talk to different kids about their ideas on all kinds of things. It would be a lot of work. You will have to think about if you have the time to do TV and keep up with your schoolwork. Of course, I would help you with the TV part."

I still can't say a word. I can't believe this is happening to me. Last year at this same time, I wasn't passing my classes. I was leaving school. Now I was in a band again. I had a boyfriend, and Inez Ramos wanted me to be on TV with her.

"Yes or no?" Inez Ramos asks.

"Yes!" I call out. "I'll do it!"

21. First Day of My Last Year in High School

The guys from KXED TV come with their truck. A woman puts make-up on me. Then they get the lights just right. I'm in the big meeting hall at Rivet High School. It is the first day of school. The first day of my last year.

We are having an all-school meeting before classes. The kids start coming into the school hall. That's when Inez Ramos says, "Go ahead. Get started. You're on the air."

I say, "This is Wilma Burns. We are live at Rivet High School as it opens for the first day of classes. Come with us to the all-school meeting."

Then everyone starts screaming and laughing. I get César to talk with me. He is all smiles. His

"This is Wilma Burns. We are live at Rivet High School as it opens for the first day of classes. Come with us to the all-school meeting."

dad comes, too. The kids all keep screaming. I wait to go on with my talk.

Way in the back of the meeting hall, I see my mom. Standing next to her is some big guy wearing white. I look harder. Is it? It is. That's my brother Levi!

I can't believe it. I think I'm going to cry right on the air. Then I think, it's my show! I can cry if I want to. So I do—a little.

At last, all the kids quiet down. Now I'm ready to talk—to all 2,000 kids before me as well as to all the others looking at KXED TV. But most of all, I talk to Levi.

Everyone is quiet and listening. I tell the story of how we came up with the idea to fight back. How we would not let them close down our school. I even tell them how I was thinking of leaving school myself. Then I tell them that the guy who gave me the first idea about all this was my brother Levi.

I make him wave from the back of the hall.

Then I tell them about my letter to him when I was really down. I tell them about his one-line letter back to me. It took me some time to think out what his letter meant. But now I know.

I raise my arm in the air and call out, "Don't get mad, get even."

All the kids scream back, "Get even!"